THERE'S A CROCODILE IN THE HOUSE

Dedicated to Michael, Heather and Willie Rain McDermott Murphy – P.C.

Dedicated to George – L.M.

Text copyright © Paul Cookson 2020
Illustrations copyright © Liz Million 2020
First published in Great Britain in 2020 by
Otter-Barry Books, Little Orchard,
Burley Gate, Herefordshire, HR1 3QS
www.otterbarrybooks.com

A catalogue record for this book is available
from the British Library

ISBN 978-1-91307-400-5

Printed in Great Britain

9 8 7 6 5 4 3 2 1

THERE'S A CROCODILE IN THE HOUSE

Poems by
PAUL COOKSON

Pictures by
LIZ MILLION

Otter-Barry BOOKS

Contents

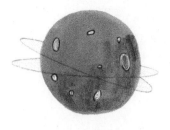

There's a Crocodile in the House!

Big sharp teeth
Open mouth
There's a crocodile in the house

I did not smile
Did not laugh
There's a crocodile in the bath

I did not know
What to think
There's a crocodile in the sink

I did not know
What to do
There's a crocodile in the loo

Face turned white
Eyes turned red
There's a crocodile in my bed

Then I did
A crazy dance
There's a crocodile in my pants

Big sharp teeth
Open mouth
There's a crocodile in the house!

Say each line for the audience to repeat – the actions
will come naturally.

Bouncy Mr Springer

He bounces when he walks
And he bounces when he talks
He bounces down the corridor
Up and down on the school hall floor
Up and down on the school hall floor

BOING! BOING! BA-DOING BOING BOING!

Up and down he bounces round
And points his bouncy finger
Best watch out when he's about
It's bouncy Mr Springer

BOING! BOING! BA-DOING BOING BOING!

He bounces in assembly
His rubber knees are trembly
You can tell where he has been
He's a human trampoline
A jumping bean on a trampoline

**BOING! BOING! BA-DOING
BOING BOING!**

He bounces here – bounces there
And he bounces... *everywhere*
Bounces on the tables – bounces on the chairs
Bounces in his clothes and in his under... *wear*
   (not really!)

BOING! BOING! BA-DOING BOING BOING!

Up and down he bounces round
And points his bouncy finger
Best watch out when he's about
It's bouncy Mr Springer!

BOING! BOING! BA-DOING BOING BOING!

It's great to have the audience join in with the
"Boing! Boing! Ba-doing Boing Boing!" and have
them jiggle their shoulders in time to the rhythm.
Also, encourage them to guess the rhymes in the
middle – always fun!

The King of All the Dinosaurs

With taloned feet and razor claws,
Leathery scales, monstrous jaws,
The king of all the dinosaurs,
Tyrannosaurus... Rex!

With sabre teeth no one ignores,
It rants and raves and royally roars,
The king of all the dinosaurs,
Tyrannosaurus... Rex!

The largest of all carnivores,
It stomps and chomps on forest floors,
The king of all the dinosaurs,
Tyrannosaurus... Rex!

Charges forwards, waging wars,
Gouges, gorges, gashes, gores,
The king of all the dinosaurs,
Tyrannosaurus... Rex!

With taloned feet and razor claws,
Leathery scales, monstrous jaws,
The king of all the dinosaurs,
Tyrannosaurus... Rex

Tyranno-ranno-ranno-ranno-ranno-saurus...
REX!

Encourage the audience to join in with the "REX" and say
it "RRREX!" and hold up their hands like dinosaur claws.

The Toilet Seat Has Teeth!

The bathroom has gone crazy,
Far beyond belief.
The sink is full of spiders... and
The toilet seat has teeth! *OW!*
The toilet seat has teeth! *OW!*

The plughole in the bath
Has a whirlpool that's beneath.
It pulls you down feet first... and
The toilet seat has teeth! *OW!*
The toilet seat has teeth! *OW!*

The toilet roll is nettles
And stings you underneath.
Makes you scream and shout... and
The toilet seat has teeth! *OW!*
The toilet seat has teeth! *OW!*

CRUNCH! SLURP!
MUNCH! BURP!
The toilet seat has teeth! *OW!*
DON'T SIT!
ON IT...
The toilet seat has teeth! *OW!*
The toilet seat has teeth! *OW!*

When you say "The toilet seat has teeth!" it's great fun
to have the audience say "OW!" and rise from their seats.

These are the Hands

These are the hands that wave
These are the hands that clap
These are the hands that pray
These are the hands that tap

These are the hands that grip
These are the hands that write
These are the hands that paint
These are the hands that fight

These are the hands that hug
These are the hands that squeeze
These are the hands that point
These are the hands that tease

These are the hands that take
These are the hands that poke
These are the hands that give
These are the hands that stroke

These are the hands that hold
These are the hands that love
These are the hands of ours
That fit us like a glove

A silent performance poem – you read each line out and the audience do the action for each line.

Friends For Ever

If you laugh
I'll laugh too

If you cry
I'll cry with you

If you're sad
I'll hold your hand

I will try
To understand

I will listen
If you talk

I will follow
When you walk

If you dance
We'll dance together

We can be
Friends for ever

Week Day Eat Days

Sunday, Sunday
Bake with Mum day

Monday, Monday
Chocolate bun day

Tuesday, Tuesday
Chicken stews day

Wednesday, Wednesday
Sweets with friends day

Thursday, Thursday
Apples and pears day

Friday, Friday
Peas and pie day

Saturday, Saturday
Let's get fatter day

Back to Sunday
Big full tum day

Robot Teachers in our School

Light-bulb eyes
Change their size
Colours flashing as she flies
Everybody's having fun
The robot teacher in Class One

Metal hair
X-ray glare
She can see things everywhere
She sees everything we do
The robot teacher in Class Two

Wires whizz
Cables fizz
We all know just who it is
Zip-zap e-lec-tric-it-y
The robot teacher in Class Three

Radar ears
They appear
Every sound is crystal clear
See her hover through the door
The robot teacher in Class Four

Big red nose
Round it goes
We're in trouble when it glows
He goes into overdrive
The robot teacher from Class Five

Memory sticks
Around his lips
Likes to chew on microchips
Keyboard teeth, a mouth that clicks
The robot teacher in Class Six

It Came from Outer Space

This is it
This is it
It came from outer space

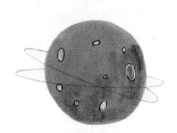

Body of a slimy snail
Flippers like a killer whale
Like a Kraken
It's attacking
With a spiky scaly tail

This is it
This is it
It came from outer space

Flies a million miles an hour
Fiery like a meteor shower
Strong and long
Like King Kong
Marvel at its mighty power

This is it
This is it
It came from outer space

Turning burning churning eyes
Growling howling yowling cries
It's a thriller
Like Godzilla
Eating planets by surprise

Ih-ih-ih
Ih-ih-ih
Ih-ih-ih-ih-ih-uhhh

Colours that you've never seen
It's part reptile part machine
Supersonic
And bionic
Massive monstrous moody mean

This is it
This is it
It came from outer space

Do the chorus in an alien voice – or sometimes just do
the rhythm with alien noises.

Beep! Beep! Whoosh!

Silver saucer shining bright
Flashing beams and laser lights
Beep! Beep! Whoosh!
Beep! Beep! Whoosh!

Faster than the speed of sound
See it spinning round and round
Beep! Beep! Whoosh!
Beep! Beep! Whoosh!

Breaking laws of gravity
Maximum velocity
Beep! Beep! Whoosh!
Beep! Beep! Whoosh!

Like a diamond in the sky
Beaming down from way on high
Beep! Beep! Whoosh!
Beep! Beep! Whoosh!

Nasty pilot, nasty crew
Coming down for me and you
Beep! Beep! Whoosh!
Beep! Beep! Whoosh....

A great one to do with a high-pitched "Beep! Beep!"
and a long, quiet "Whoosh!"

My Brother Pete and his Stinky Feet!

Oh no! Stinky Pete!
My brother Pete and his stinky feet!

When you see his monkey toes
You just have to hold your nose

When he goes outside to play
All the pigs run away

Oh no! Stinky Pete!
My brother Pete and his stinky feet!

Everyone has gas masks on
We all wear them till he's gone

When he goes outside to play
All the skunks run away

Oh no! Stinky Pete!
My brother Pete and his stinky feet!

OH NO! STINKY PETE!
MY BROTHER PETE AND HIS STINKY FEET!

A fun one – especially if you hold your noses while saying the chorus!

Dad's BIG Toe

Dad can wriggle his big toe
Once for yes and twice for no
It may be just one of five
But it's the one that comes alive

Like a massive monkey nut
It sticks out from his foot
Uh-oh… Oh no!
Dad's BIG toe

It swivels and it wiggles
Always on the go
It dances and it jiggles
Dad's BIG toe

It shivers and it shakes
Twitches to and fro
It quivers and it quakes
Dad's BIG toe

It's horrible and hairy
And wobbles high and low
It's scaly and it's scary
Dad's BIG toe

It lights up in the night
A green and ghostly glow
And gives us all a fright
Dad's **BIG** toe

Like a massive monkey nut
It sticks out from his foot
Uh-oh... Oh no!
Dad's BIG toe

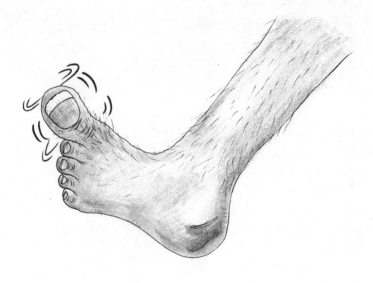

I'd Rather Be a Footballer

Stuck in class – doing maths
Staring at the wall
I'd rather be a footballer
Kicking my foot...

I'll blast it and I'll pass it
Leave them feeling small
I'd rather be a footballer
Kicking my foot...

I'll flick it up and kick it up
Beating one and all
I'd rather be a footballer
Kicking my foot...

It's fun for the audience to join in with the last syllable
or word of every verse (football).

Animals Don't Wear Clothes

You can't put socks on a snail
You can't put pants on a whale

A butterfly can't wear a shirt
You can't put a squid in a skirt

You can't put wellies on a llama
A shark won't wear a pink pyjama

You can't put a slug in a three-piece suit
A worm can't wear a football boot

You can't put flippers on a dog
Or roller skates on a frog

Most have coats as anyone knows
But animals don't
Animals don't
Animals don't wear clothes

Call the Vet!

Don't put the cat in Grandma's hat
Don't put the dog in the dishwasher
Don't put the snake in a wedding cake
That's no place to put a pet!

Call the vet
Call the vet
That's no place to put a pet!

Don't put the rabbit on the roof
Don't put the budgie in the bath
Don't put the tortoise in the toilet
That's no place to put a pet!

Call the vet
Call the vet
That's no place to put a pet!

Don't put the goldfish in the sink
Don't put the gerbil in the jam
Don't put a parrot in your pants
That's no place to put a pet!

Call the vet
Call the vet
That's no place to put a pet!

Mrs Silver

No scars upon her cheek
No shiny silver hook
No clip-clop wooden leg
But if you take a closer look...

There's no parrot on her shoulder
There's no beard, wild and hairy
There's no eye-patch on her eye
But there's something strange and scary

She doesn't say "A-harr-harr-harr!"
Or sing along "Yo-ho-ho-ho"
She doesn't even have a ship
But there's something different that we know

Maybe it's the stripy tights
The spotty scarf that's red and white

When she walks the way she jangles
All the bracelets, all the bangles

Rings on fingers, thumbs and toes
Or the jewel through her nose

The solid silver earring hoops
The black and shiny buckled boots

Perhaps a mixture of them all
And the map up on the classroom wall

She gazes at it such a lot
Especially where "X" marks the spot

We see how much she does desire it
We think Miss Silver is a ....

The audience can call out the
last word of the poem (pirate).

Sea Shanty Pirate Chant

Got my eye-patch
Got my parrot
Got my beard
Got my hook

Yo ho ho! Yo ho ho!
Big bad pirates, off we go!

Got my sword
Got my hat
Got my treasure
Got my map

Yo ho ho! Yo ho ho!
Big bad pirates, off we go!

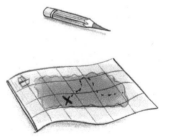

Got my leg
It is wooden
Got my ship
It's a good'un

Yo ho ho! Yo ho ho!
Big bad pirates, off we go!

Got my cannon
I can fire it
Now I'm ready!
I'm a pirate!

Yo ho ho! Yo ho ho!
Big bad pirates, off we go!

Yo ho ho!
Yarrr!

Put on yer best pirate voice! *Aharr!*

Picture This

Cover your eyes and don't take a look
Imagine the stories inside the book
Picture the pages, the words we have read
Bring them to life – inside your head

Think of the colours, think of the features
The people, the pets, the monsters and creatures
Think of the mountains, the sea and the sky
Perfectly pictured – in your mind's eye

The wand of a wizard, glowing with light
The scar on his forehead, zig-zag and bright
The snow in the wardrobe, glistening white
The eyes of a dragon, blazing at night

A bear in a scarf, a cat in a hat
An elephant patched, a Stanley that's flat
A pea-green boat, a flying umbrella
A hungry hairy caterpillar

The hunt for a bear, a Gruffalo's nose
A haunted house where nobody goes
A park keeper's hut, a puppy called Kipper
An apple, a witch, one glass slipper

A giant so friendly, funny and big
A wolf on a search for a girl or a pig
Dinosaurs, pirates, aliens too
A boy who's called Henry, a teddy called Pooh

Yes, cover your eyes and don't take a look
Mix up the stories from every book
Picture the pages, the words we've all read
And bring them to life... inside your head

Who Am I?

(A Kenning)

Stripy pullover
Sharp stinger
Buzzing buzzer
Honey bringer

The Skipping-Rope Queen

I never slide and never slip
Never tumble, never trip
Never tangle, never fall
Never get tied up at all
I'm the fastest ever seen
I'm the playtime skipping queen

Playground Song

Round and round the roundabouts
Fast and slow
Sliding down the slides
High to low
Swinging on the swings
To and fro
Playing in the playground
Watch me go!

Raining on the Trip

It's raining on the trip
Raining on the trip
Drip drip drip
Raining on the trip

It's never going to stop
Never going to stop
Drop drop drop
Never going to stop

I haven't got a coat
Haven't got a coat
Splish splash splosh
Going to get soaked

I think it's going to flood
Think it's going to flood
Thud thud thud
Think it's going to flood

The clouds are getting dark
Clouds are getting dark
Any more rain
We're going to need an ark

It's raining on the trip
Raining on the trip
Drip drip drip
Raining on the trip

It's never going to stop
Never going to stop
Drop drop drop
Never going to stop

Drop drop drop
Never going to stop
Drop drop drop
Never going to...

This works well if you have the audience repeat the last two lines of each verse.

The Day We Built the Snowman

Round and round the garden,
Rolling up the snow.
One step – two step,
Watch the snowman grow.

Round and round the garden,
Us and Dad and Mum,
Building up the snowman,
Having lots of fun.

Mum has got a carrot,
Dad has got a pipe,
Sister's got a scarf
To keep him warm at night.

Baseball cap and shades,
Trainers for his feet,
The day we built the snowman,
The coolest in the street.

Round and round the garden
In the winter weather,
The day we built the snowman,
Having fun together.

Round and round the garden,
Rolling up the snow.
One step – two step,
Watch the snowman grow.

Round and round the garden,
Us and Dad and Mum,
Building up the snowman,
Having lots of fun!

There's an Alien Under My Bed!

There's an alien under my bed, Mum,
An alien under my bed.
It's green and purple and red, Mum,
The alien under my bed.

There's an alien under my bed, Mum,
An alien under my bed.
It smells like something dead, Mum,
The alien under my bed.

There's an alien under my bed, Mum,
An alien under my bed.
It's wanting to be fed, Mum,
The alien under my bed.

It's making scary noises, Mum,
It's got an ugly head.
It's wiggling and wriggling,
The alien under my bed

There's an alien under my bed, Mum,
It's trying to steal my cover.
Er... I was wrong with what I said, Mum,
It's just my little brother!

Animal Confusion

There's a wolf with the head of a whale
A shark with a waggy tail

A monkey with a long grey trunk
A cat that smells like a skunk

A giraffe with a hippo's head
And a mouse with an elephant's legs

A parrot with crocodile jaws
An octopus with a tiger's claws

A porcupine covered in fluff
A snake with a shell so tough

They may all be mixed up
Confusing all of us
But nothing's as confusing as…
A duck-billed platypus!

The Dinner Lady Dragon Queen

She may be big
She may be green
But she's not nasty
Loud or mean
She's the best that's ever been
The Dinner Lady Dragon Queen

Her nostrils flame
There's fire and steam
But no one's scared
And no one screams
She's the best we've ever seen
The Dinner Lady Dragon Queen

She breathes out smoke
Flames and heat
To cook the food
That we all eat
She's the leader of the team
The Dinner Lady Dragon Queen

Eyes that twinkle
Wings that soar
In the hall
And corridor
A tail to wipe each table clean
The Dinner Lady Dragon Queen

She's a beast
But she's the best
A dragon in
A hat and dress
Sweet and kind, a daytime dream
The Dinner Lady Dragon Queen

The T Rex Rocks

A dinosaur party down by the lake
A rumble in the jungle starting to shake
A tremble in the air, like an earthquake
Everything stops...

When the T Rex Rocks!

Loud, loud sound of heavy-metal thunder
Dancing to the sound, a rock and roll number
Brontosaurus breaks into a rhumba
Everything stops...

When the T Rex Rocks!

When the T Rex rocks, mountains crumble
Leaves all shake and treetops tumble
Boulders roll, stones all rumble
Everything stops...

When the T Rex Rocks

A clickety-click of his ten-ton claws
The growl and the howl from his mighty jaws
The dinosaurs roar their wild applause
Everything stops...

When the T Rex Rocks!

Freeze and make a dinosaur face after "Everything stops..." in each verse.

The Model We're Making in Class with Miss

Scissors, glue, yogurt pots
Sellotape, a cornflake box
Egg cartons and bottle tops
Rubber gloves and Dad's old socks

Cardboard, hardboard
And my brother's dartboard
Polythene, plasticine
And my mother's magazine

Walking sticks, building bricks
Lipsticks, Pritt sticks
Silly string, safety pins
Lots and lots of other things

Plastic, elastic
We're enthusiastic
Mould it and fold it
Then we'll plaster-cast it
Paint and stain it
It'll be fantastic

Add a bit of that, then a bit of this
For the model we're making in class with Miss
Stick it on that, stick it on this
For the model we're making in class with Miss
The model we're making
The model we're making
The model we're making in class with Miss

Jumble in the Jungle

Way down in the jungle
Everything has changed
Everything is different
Things are very strange

Elephants fly way up high
Sad hyenas sob and cry

Giraffes all burrow under ground
Silent parrots make no sound

Alligators climb up trees
Snakes have all grown hairy knees

Lizards swing from vine to vine
Gorillas leave a trail of slime

Rhinos wriggle in the river
Hippos hiss and slide and slither

Speedy sloths are running races
Lions are making funny faces

All the zebras now have spots
Leopards – stripes instead of dots

Yes, everything has changed
Way down in the jungle
Things are very strange
In the jungle jumble

The Warty Hog

The Warty Hog,
A pig of sorts,
Has purple pimples,
Hairy warts.

It sniffles, snorts,
Sits on a log,
The sniffy, snorty
Warty Hog.

It sits and splashes
In the bog,
The stinky, smelly
Warty Hog.

The Porky Pine

The Porky Pine
A prickly swine
A beast that no one likes

No friend of mine
The Porky Pine
A pig all covered in spikes

The Hippopotamouse

He'll smash the doors and break the walls
If he gets in your house
There's no trap that's big enough
For the Hippopotamouse

The Chimpanzeel

The Chimpanzeel
Has a slippery feel,
Long and thin and quite unreal.

Swings through trees,
Swims through seas,
The cheeky-chappy Chimpanzeel.

Lowena

A little like the hyena
But never seen at all
They're very, very, very, very, very
Very, very small

The Gorillama

A creature full of drama
Is the woolly Gorillama
It spits and swings and swings and spits
And is certainly no charmer

Welly Walk

We're going on a welly walk!
A splishy splashy welly walk!
We've got wellies!
Big strong wellies!

Yuck! Mud!
Mucky muddy mud!
But we don't care
We've got wellies
Big strong wellies
SQUISH-SQUASH-SQUISH-SQUASH-SQUELCHY-SQUELCH!

We're going on a welly walk!
A splishy splashy welly walk!

Here we go
Cold new snow
But we don't care
We've got wellies
Big strong wellies
SCRUNCH -SCRUNCH-SWISH-SWISH-SWISH

We're going on a welly walk!
A splishy splashy welly walk!
Ice! Nice
Slippery shiny ice
But we don't care
We've got wellies
Big strong wellies
SL-I-I-PPY SLI-I-IDY KE-RICK KE-RACKKKK

We're going on a welly walk!
A splishy splashy welly walk!

Uh-oh – a ditch
A deep dirty ditch
But we don't care
We've got wellies
Big strong wellies
JUMP! SPLADOOSH! SPLAT! SPLAT!

We're going on a welly walk!
A splishy splashy welly walk!

Ah – a forest
Leaves and twigs
But we don't care
We've got wellies
Big strong wellies
SNIPPETY – SNAP! CRUNCH CRUNCH CRUNCH!

Yucky mud
SQUISH-SQUASH-SQUISH-SQUASH-SQUELCHY-SQUELCH!

Cold, cold snow
SCRUNCH -SCRUNCH-SWISH-SWISH-SWISH

Nice and shiny ice
SL-I-I-PPY SLI-I-IDDY KE-RICK KE-RACKKKK

Deep dirty ditch
JUMP! SPLADOOSH! SPLAT ! SPLAT!

Autumn forest
SNIPPETY – SNAP! CRUNCH!
CRUNCH!CRUNCH!

We're going on a welly walk!
A splishy splashy welly walk!
We've got wellies!
Big strong wellies!

Repeat each line and do all the actions and noises!

The Day the Mouse Came into Class

It only gave a tiny squeak!
Our teacher screamed,
Our teacher shrieked –
The day the mouse came into class.

It only stopped to sit and stare.
Our teacher jumped
Onto her chair –
The day the mouse came into class.

It sat upon the window sill.
Our teacher just
Could not stay still –
The day the mouse came into class.

It looked around, squeaked once more,
Then ran out through
The classroom door –
The day the mouse came into class.

The beast had gone, the coast was clear.
Her shaking stopped,
She dried her tear –
The day the mouse came into class.

Our teacher stepped down from her chair,
Changed her lesson, then and there.
Gave out pencils, papers for
The picture we all had to draw...

The Day the Mouse Came into Class!

Who Was It?

Who put Grandad's slippers in the fridge?
Who put Sister's homework in the tree?
Who put Brother's football in the bath?
We-e-ell...
Just who could it be?

Who put Granny's hat on the cat?
Who threw Dad's phone in the sea
Who put lipstick on the dog?
We-e-ell...
Just who could it be?

Who put jelly in Uncle's shoes?
Who let Auntie's budgie fly free?
Who put a real live worm on the pasta?
We-e-ell ...
Just who could it be?

Who ate the icing on the cake?
Who drew a face on the TV?
Who put cream in Mummy's tights?
We-e-ell
We-e-ell
We-e-ell

OK, it was me!

Bottoms!

Bottoms! Bottoms!
Children – on your **bottoms!**
Bottoms! Bottoms!
Children – on your **bottoms!**

Lots of bottoms through the door
Lots of bottoms on the floor
Lots of bottoms wall to wall
Lots of bottoms fill the hall
Bottoms that are wriggling
Bottoms that are wiggling
Bottoms that are slithering
Fidgeting and jiggling

Bottoms! Bottoms!
Children – on your **bottoms!**
Bottoms! Bottoms!
Children – on your **bottoms!**

Bottoms that are twitching
Bottoms that are itching
Bottoms that are slipping
Bottoms that are tipping
Wobble bottoms
Jelly bottoms

Wriggle bottoms
Smelly bottoms

Bottoms! Bottoms!
Children – on your **bottoms!**
Bottoms! Bottoms!
Children – on your **bottoms!**

Introduce this as a poem about an infant teacher's
favourite word and encourage the audience to join in
with the word "Bottoms" – guaranteed hilarity.

Wrigglebum John

Wrigglebum John
Wrigglebum John
He's got a chair that he won't sit on

Fidget left
Fidget right
Fidget through the day and the night

Wrigglebum John
Wrigglebum John
He's got a chair that he won't sit on

Every day
Hour and minute
He's got a chair but he won't stay in it

On the tables watch him crawl
Climbing up and down the wall
Swinging on the lights and curtains
Of one thing you can be certain
Jumping, running, skipping, hopping
You have not a chance of stopping

Wrigglebum John
Wrigglebum John
He's got a chair that he won't sit on

Now he's here
Now he's gone
Doesn't stay around for long

Where does he get his energy from?
Wrigglebum Wrigglebum Wrigglebum John
Wrigglebum Wrigglebum Wrigglebum John
Wrigglebum Wrigglebum Wrigglebum…
JOHN!

Have the audience join in with "John".

The Secrets that My Hamster Knows

Late at night when I'm alone
And everyone is fast asleep
I talk to my pet hamster
Squeak! Squeak! Squeak!

I know you don't believe me
But he listens when I speak
Just the way he stops and stares
Squeak! Squeak! Squeak!

All my secrets safely stored
Like food inside his cheek
No one's ever finding out
Squeak! Squeak! Squeak!

Every little secret story
Safe and sound to keep
He won't say a single word
Squeak! Squeak! Squeak!

Even if he makes a noise
Strong and loud or weak
The only sound you'll ever hear is
Squeak! Squeak! Squeak...
Squeak... Squeak!

My Dog Kenning

Stick fetcher
Ear twitcher
Carpet scratcher
Flea itcher

Biscuit stealer
Tongue slobberer
Smell maker
Cat botherer

Football chaser
High-pitched howler
Staircase racer
Deep growler

Tail wagger
Noisy barker
Slipper chewer
Sofa parker

Mummy's Yummy Cheese on Toast

One of the things I like the most
Is my mummy's cheese on toast
I love to see it melt and ooze
It's the thing I love to choose
Better than a Sunday roast
Mummy's yummy cheese on toast

Magic, Near and Faraway

There's a place we like to meet
A special place we play
It's magical, mysterious
It's near and faraway

Sometimes it's a castle

Full of queens and kings
Sometimes it's a jungle
Where cheeky monkeys swing

Sometimes it's a mountain
The highest in the world
Others it's a pirate ship
With flags and sails unfurled

A supersonic rocket
That's landed on the sun
And then it is a circus tent
Wires high to balance on

A T-Rex skeleton

Prehistoric bone
A dragon's lair, a graveyard where
The monsters turn to stone

Sometimes it is just a tree
That we all rush to climb
Always just the place to be
Where we lose track of time

Magic, near and faraway
The place for you and me
The tree that is whatever
We imagine it to be

Acknowledgements

Special thanks to Gaby Morgan and Macmillan Children's Books, as versions of the following poems first appeared in *Paul Cookson's Joke Shop, The Very Best Of Paul Cookson* and *I'd Rather Be A Footballer:* Bouncy Mr Springer, The King of All the Dinosaurs, The Toilet Seat Has Teeth, These Are the Hands, I'd Rather Be a Footballer, Raining on the Trip, The Day We Built the Snowman, The Model We're Making In Class with Miss, Bottoms and Wrigglebum John. Versions of It Came From Outer Space and Beep! Beep! Whoosh! first appeared in *It Came From Outer Space* by Paul Cookson and David Harmer (Macmillan Children's Books). The T Rex Rocks was written by Paul Cookson with Stan Cullimore.

About the author

 **Paul Cookson** has been a poet for a very long time now, has published over 50 books and sold over a million copies. His work has taken him all over the world. As well as being Poet in Residence for the National Football Museum, he is Writer in Residence for *Sing Together* and *Everton In The Community* and one third of the musical group, *Don Powell's Occasional Flames.* He is married with two grown-up children, one dog and eight ukuleles and he lives in Nottinghamshire.

For more information you can look at his website and follow him on twitter:
www.paulcooksonpoet.co.uk
Twitter @paulcooksonpoet

☆ About the illustrator ☆

**Liz Million** is a lively illustrator and author of children's books and she likes to think that she has THE best job in the world. When she isn't painting and writing books in her little studio in north-east England, she spends a lot of time travelling the world, talking to children in amazing schools, libraries and museums! Her favourite things to draw with children are cartoony animals and crazy creatures.

Liz graduated from Kingston-upon-Thames University in 1998 with a degree in Illustration and has been illustrating and writing ever since. She loves living in Darlington, County Durham, with her husband, her son, George, and her cute Bedlington terrier, Peggy.

For more information you can look at her website and follow her on twitter and facebook:
www.lizmillion.com
Twitter @liz_million
Facebook Liz Million Illustrator/Author Page

MORE GREAT POETRY FROM
OTTER-BARRY BOOKS

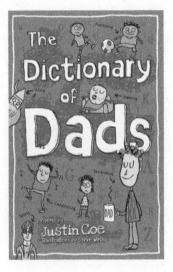

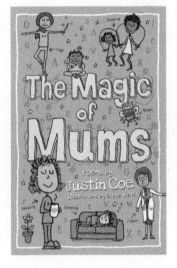

The Dictionary of Dads
9781910959169

the Magic of Mums
9781910959640